Writing
Readiness

K

Table of Contents

- Print Aa to Zz plus letter fun
- Pencil control activities
- Sight words, rhyming
- Beginning story writing, letters, lists
- And much more!

Margaret Ann Hawkins, B.Ed.

Getting Ready For Writing

Use your finger, then a pencil, to follow each pet to its home.

Getting Ready For Writing

Use your finger, then a pencil, to help each animal find its home.

Getting Ready For Writing

Use your finger, then a pencil, to drive each vehicle on the road to the garage. Don't touch the sides of the road!

Getting Ready For Writing

Draw curved lines to the pencil cases
with your finger then a pencil.
Don't touch the lines!

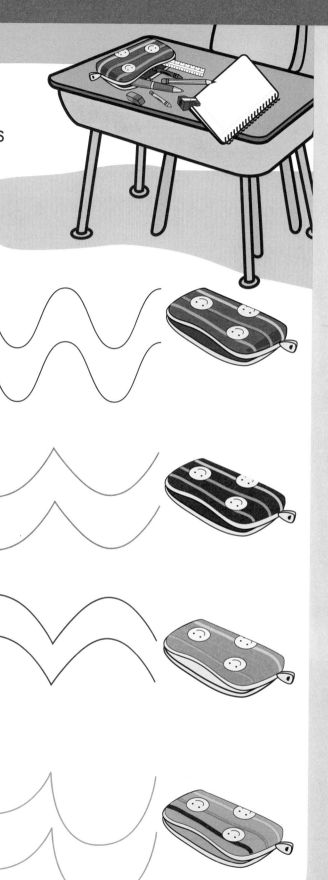

Printing and Letter Sounds

Start

Follow the arrows with your finger, then a pencil.

Trace and print A and **a**. Say the letter sound.

Circle the things that start with **a**.

airplane

ant

campfire

apple

alligator

beaver

Printing and Letter Sounds

Start

Follow the arrows with your finger, then a pencil.

Trace and print B and b. Say the letter sound.

B B B B B B B B

B

b b b b b b b b b

b

Circle the things that start with b.

bear

balloon

tree

book

ball

boat

Printing and Letter Sounds

Start

Follow the arrows with your finger, then a pencil.

Trace and print C and c. Say the letter sound.

Circle the things that start with c.

candle   car   fish   carrot

Printing and Letter Sounds

Start

Follow the arrows with your finger, then a pencil.

Trace and print D and d. Say the letter sound.

D D D D D D D D D D

D

d d d d d d d d d d d d d d

d

Circle the things that start with d.

dog

deer

house

dime

dinosaur

polar bear

Printing and Letter Sounds

Follow the arrows with your finger, then a pencil.

Start

Trace and print E and **e**. Say the letter sound.

E E E E E E E E E E

E

e e e e e e e e e e e e

e

Colour things that start with **e**.

egg

elephant

butterfly

ear

Printing and Letter Sounds

Follow the arrows with your finger, then a pencil.

Trace and print F and f. Say the letter sound.

Colour things that start with f.

fish

truck

flag

frog

11

Draw a line from the picture to the letter it **starts** with.
Print the letter.

a ‾‾‾‾‾‾‾‾‾‾‾‾‾‾‾‾

f _f_ ‾‾‾‾‾‾‾‾‾‾‾

c ‾‾‾‾‾‾‾‾‾‾‾‾‾‾‾‾

b ‾‾‾‾‾‾‾‾‾‾‾‾‾‾‾‾

e ‾‾‾‾‾‾‾‾‾‾‾‾‾‾‾‾

d ‾‾‾‾‾‾‾‾‾‾‾‾‾‾‾‾

Printing and Letter Sounds

Start

Follow the arrows with your finger, then a pencil.

Trace and print G and g. Say the letter sound.

G G G G G G G G G

g g g g g g g g g g

Circle the things that start with g.

goat   gloves   goldfish   sun

Printing and Letter Sounds

Follow the arrows with your finger, then a pencil.

Trace and print H and **h**. Say the letter sound.

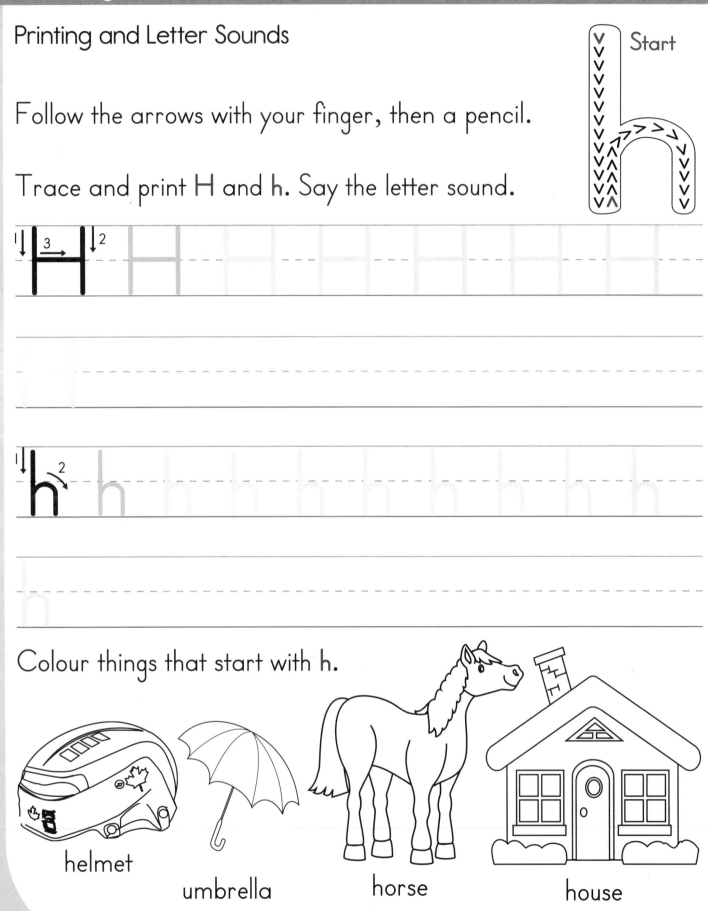

Colour things that start with **h**.

helmet

umbrella

horse

house

Printing and Letter Sounds

Follow the arrows with your finger, then a pencil.

Trace and print I and i. Say the letter sound.

Circle the things that start with i.

iron

insect

inukshuk

pizza

ice cream

icicles

igloo

Printing and Letter Sounds

Follow the arrows with your finger, then a pencil.

Trace and print J and j. Say the letter sound.

Start

J

j

Circle the things that start with j.

jam

calculator

jack-o-lantern

juggle

juice

jacket

Printing and Letter Sounds

Start

Follow the arrows with your finger, then a pencil.

Trace and print K and k. Say the letter sound.

Circle the things that start with k.

apple

keys

ambulance

kite

grapes

17

Printing and Letter Sounds

Start

Follow the arrows with your finger, then a pencil.

Trace and print L and l. Say the letter sound.

Circle the things that start with l.

leaf

bee

lemon

lamp

lock

ladder

Review g–l

Draw a line from the picture to the letter it starts with.
Print the letter.

g

i

j

j

h   h

l

k

Printing and Letter Sounds

Start

Follow the arrows with your finger, then a pencil.

Trace and print M and m. Say the letter sound.

M M M M M M M M M

M

m m m m m m m m m

m

Draw 2 things that start with m.

moose   mouse

Printing and Letter Sounds

Start

Follow the arrows with your finger, then a pencil.

Trace and print N and n. Say the letter sound.

Draw 2 things that start with n.

nuts   net

Printing and Letter Sounds

Start

Follow the arrows with your finger, then a pencil.

Trace and print O and o. Say the letter sound.

Colour things that start with o.

orange

kite

off and on

olive

owl

Printing and Letter Sounds

Start

Follow the arrows with your finger, then a pencil.

Trace and print P and **p.** Say the letter sound.

P P P P P P P P P P

P

p p p p p p p p p p

p

Colour the things that start with **p.**

hay   pizza   pencil

pig

Printing and Letter Sounds

Start

Follow the arrows with your finger, then a pencil.

Trace and print Q and q. Say the letter sound.

Q Q Q Q Q Q Q

q q q q q q q q q q

Circle the things that start with q.

quarter

truck

queen

goose

quilt

Printing and Letter Sounds

Start

Follow the arrows with your finger, then a pencil.

Trace and print R and r. Say the letter sound.

R R R R R R R R R

R

r r r r r r r r r r r r r

r

Circle the things that start with r.

raspberries   rock   bear   radish

25

Review m–r

Draw a line from the picture to the letter it **starts** with.
Print the letter.

m _____

o _____   O

q _____

n _____

r _____

p _____

Printing and Letter Sounds

Start

Follow the arrows with your finger, then a pencil.

Trace and print S and s. Say the letter sound.

S̃ S S S S S S S

s̃ s s s s s

Draw 2 things that start with s.

snowy owl   snail

Printing and Letter Sounds

Start

Follow the arrows with your finger, then a pencil.

Trace and print T and t. Say the letter sound.

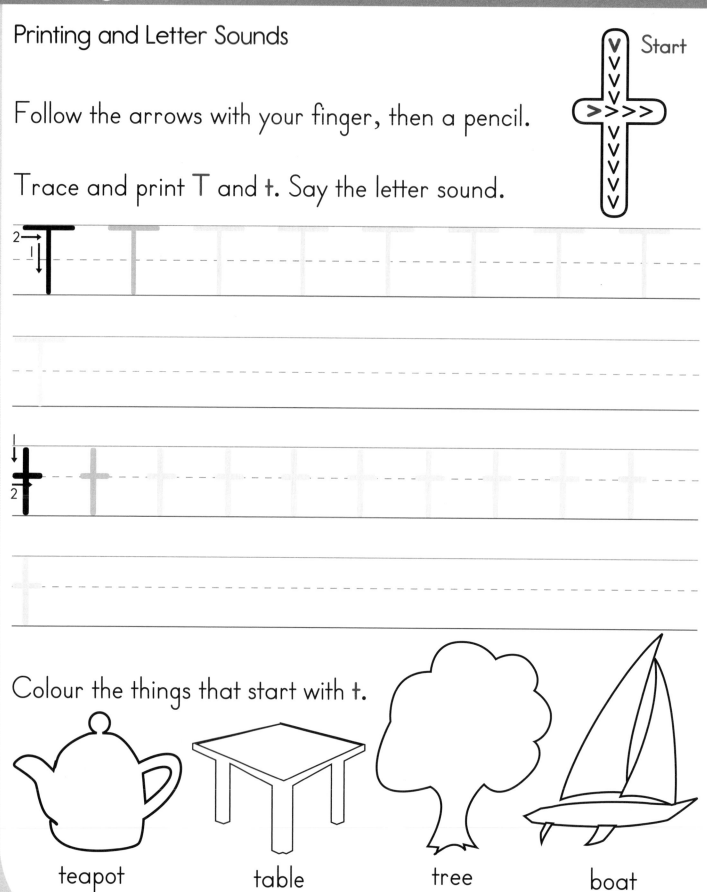

Colour the things that start with t.

teapot   table   tree   boat

Printing and Letter Sounds

Start

Follow the arrows with your finger, then a pencil.

Trace and print U and u. Say the letter sound.

Put a ✔ on things that start with u.

up

UP

umbrella

apple

unicorn

uniform

arm

toy

Printing and Letter Sounds

Start

Follow the arrows with your finger, then a pencil.

Trace and print V and v. Say the letter sound.

Put a ✔ on things that start with v.

violin

train

vacuum

fingerprint

volcano

vest

vase

Printing and Letter Sounds

Follow the arrows with your finger, then a pencil.

Start

Trace and print W and w. Say the letter sound.

Colour the things that start with w.

wagon

worm

watch

rabbit

watermelon

Printing and Letter Sounds   Start

Follow the arrows with your finger, then a pencil.

Trace and print X and x. Say the letter sound.

Colour the things that start or end with x.

socks

six

x-ray

xylophone

box

32

Learning About Letters

Review s–x

Draw a line from the picture to the letter it starts with.
Print the letter.

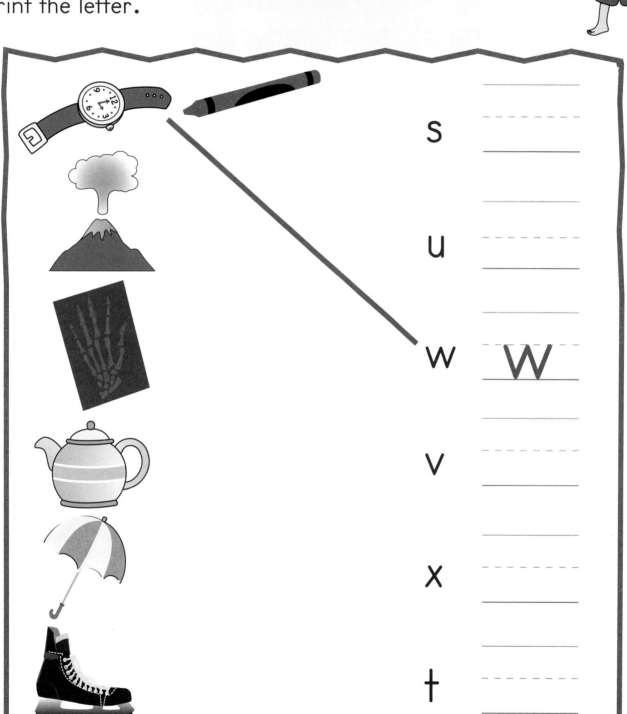

s _____

u _____

w W _____

v _____

x _____

t _____

Printing and Letter Sounds

Follow the arrows with your finger, then a pencil.

Trace and print Y and y. Say the letter sound.

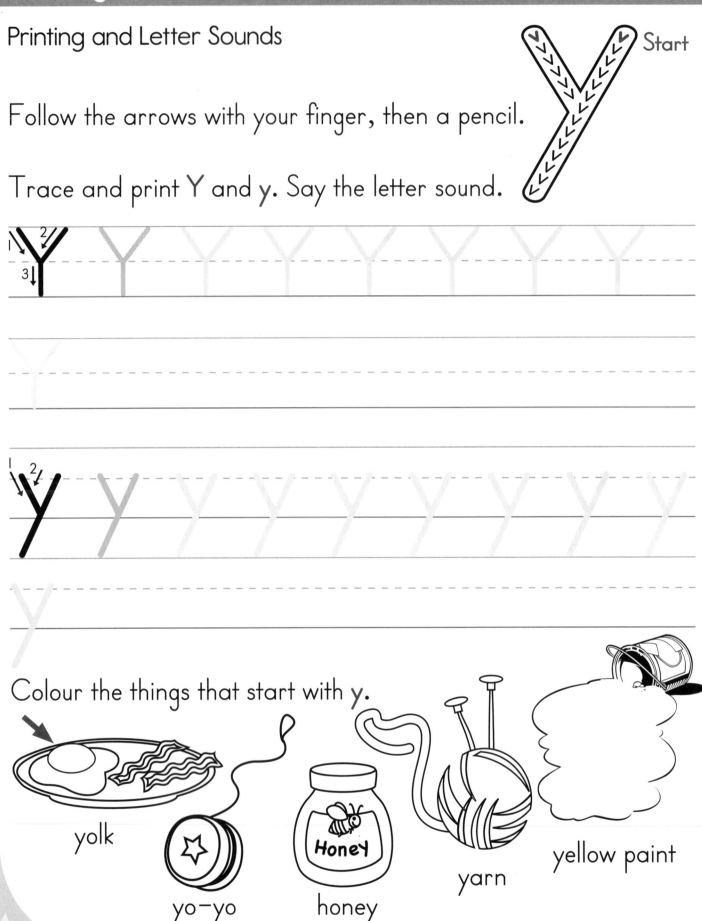

Colour the things that start with y.

yolk

yo-yo

honey

yarn

yellow paint

Printing and Letter Sounds

Follow the arrows with your finger, then a pencil.

Trace and print Z and z. Say the letter sound.

Start

Circle the things that start with z.

zero

zigzag

zebra

zoo

zipper

stroller

sun

35

Alphabetical Order Maze

Follow the alphabet path with your finger then a pencil.
Try not to touch the sides or the letters!

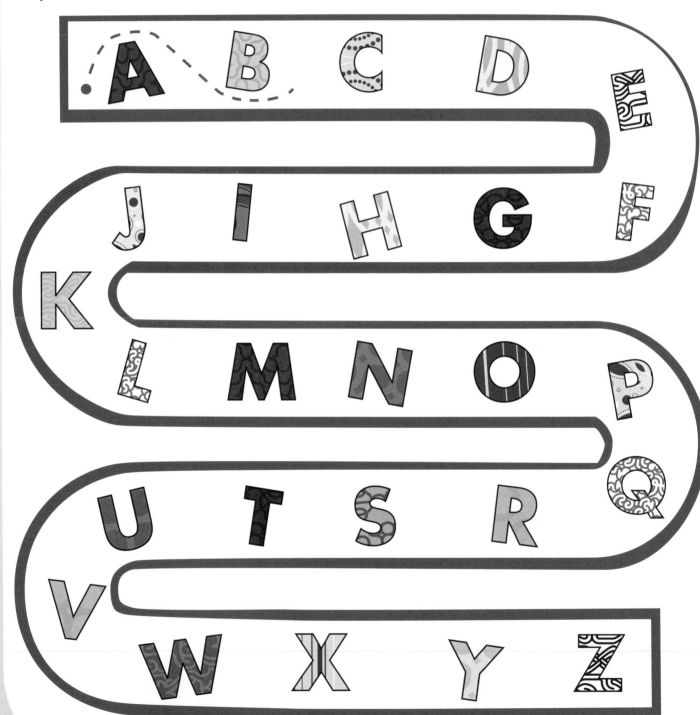

Use a pencil to follow the dots from **a** to **z**.

Colour the picture.

Start

Alphabet Review

Circle the beginning letter.

Example:

a   v   (f)

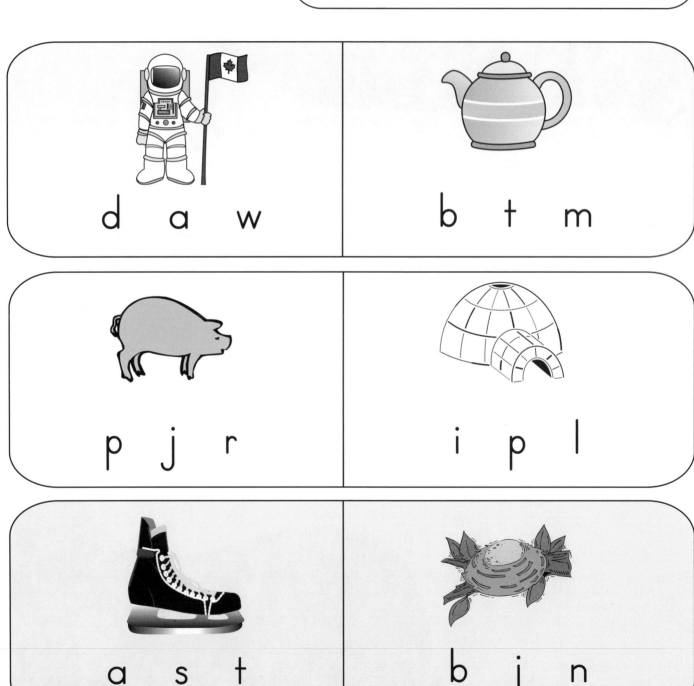

d   a   w

b   t   m

p   j   r

i   p   l

a   s   t

b   j   n

Alphabet Review

Circle the beginning letter.

Example:

z   a   (k)

d   l   a

g   p   s

v   t   f

b   d   g

o   a   h

w   u   f

Alphabet Review

Print the first letter.

c e h r m d

Example:

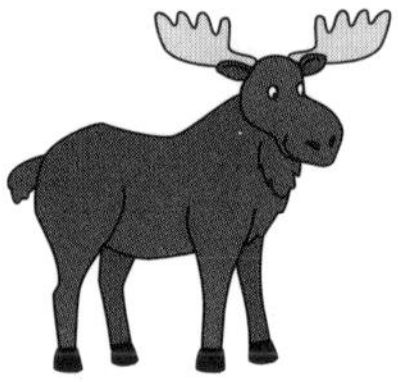

m

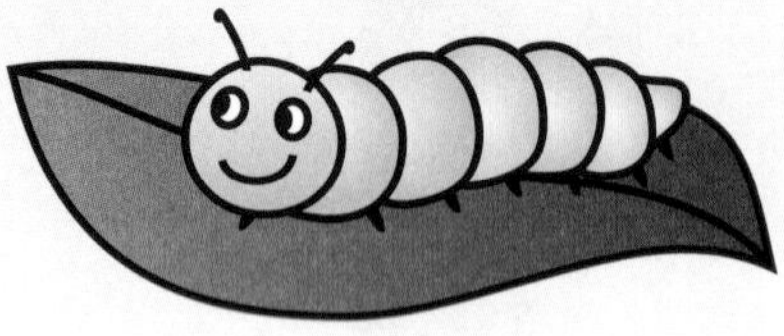

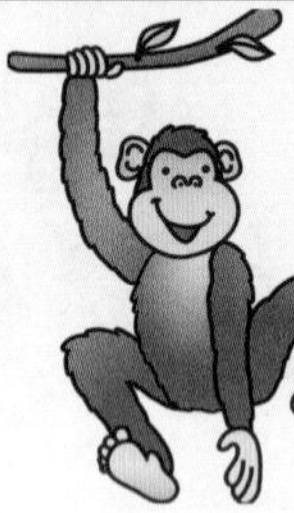

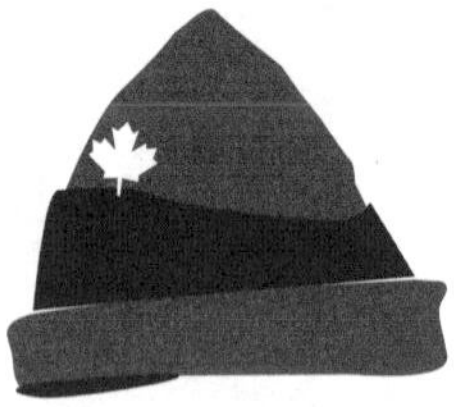

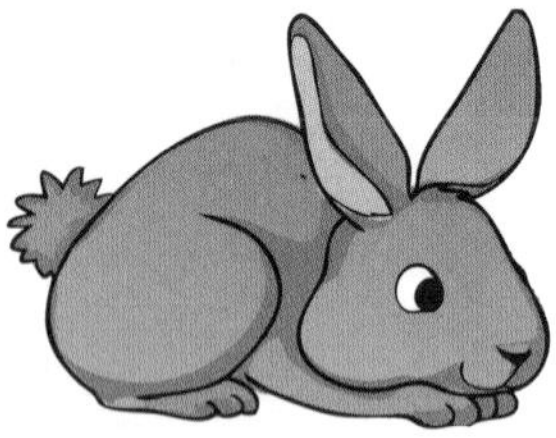

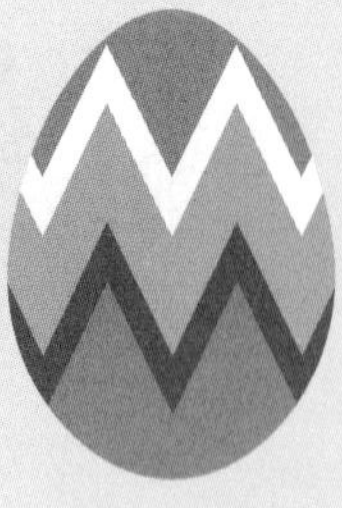

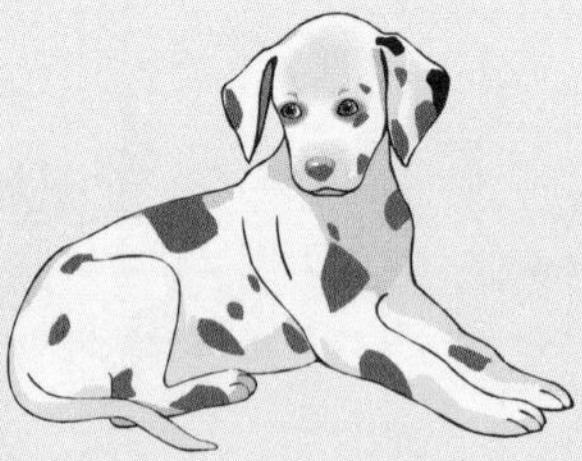

Alphabet Review

Print the first letter.

q u j z w v y x

Example:

_____

z

Rhyme Time

Rhyming words start with different sounds and end with the same sound. Draw a line to each rhyming pair.

hat	house
mouse	three
tree	pan
pie	frog
fan	cat
log	tie
pen	car
jar	ten

Rhyme Time

Read the words from the rhyming word families.

at

sat
cat
hat
mat
rat
pat

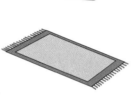

ap

cap
map
lap
nap
tap
gap

en

den
pen
men
hen
ten

an

can
man
fan
tan
ran
van

et

pet
get
wet
met
let
yet

ut

but
cut
hut
nut
gut
rut

in

pin
tin
win
fin
bin
din

ot

dot
got
hot
not
pot
lot

it

hit
pit
sit
bit
fit
kit

Rhyme Time

Make rhyming words by adding the letter on the left to the pair of letters on the right. Say each word.

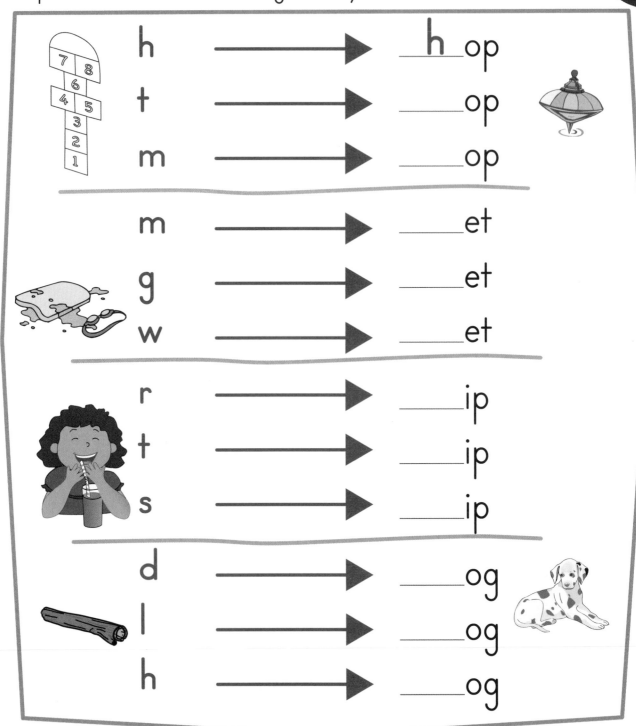

h ——————▶ h op

t ——————▶ ___op

m ——————▶ ___op

m ——————▶ ___et

g ——————▶ ___et

w ——————▶ ___et

r ——————▶ ___ip

t ——————▶ ___ip

s ——————▶ ___ip

d ——————▶ ___og

l ——————▶ ___og

h ——————▶ ___og

Super Sight Words

Here are some words to help you write stories.

Print each word.

Draw a line to the matching word.

Working with Words

More Super Sight Words

Here are some more words to help write stories.
Print each word.
Draw a line to the matching word.

and	and	you
see		me
me		look
to		see
look		and
you		to

I Can Write Sentences

Look at the picture. Read and print the sentence.

I see my house.

Look at the cake.

I Can Write Sentences

Look at the picture. Read and print the sentence.

I am playing at the park.

I see you and me.

I Can Write Sentences

Look at the picture. Read the sentence and fill in the missing letters. Print the sentence.

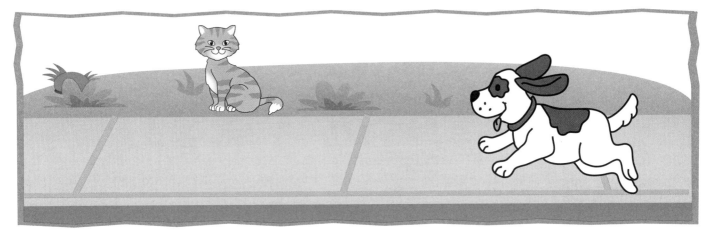

I see a d _ _ _ and a c _ _ _ .

_____

- -

_____

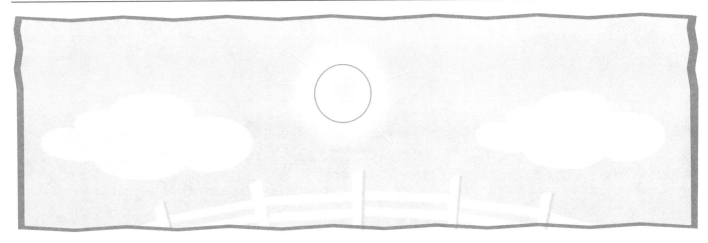

The s _ _ _ is in t _ _ _ sky.

_____

- -

_____

I Can Write Sentences

Look at the picture. Read the sentence and fill in the missing letters. Print the sentence.

The boat __ __ __ on __ __ __ __ lake.

_____

_____

T__ __ __ bird is up __ __ __ the tree.

_____

_____

All About Me

Write about you. Draw pictures to match.

This is me!

I am _____ years old.

This is where I live!

My address is _____

_____

About My Family

Write about your family. Draw a picture to match.

About My Family!

There are _____ people in my family.
Here are their names.

_____

_____

_____

_____

_____

_____

_____

_____

_____

A Letter

Write a letter to someone special. Then draw a picture.

_____

Dear _____ ,

_____

_____

_____

_____

_____

Please write back to me.
From,

_____

A Shopping List

It is time to go shopping.
Make a list to tell what you want to buy.

milk

eggs

bananas

apple

Grocery List

cereal

carrots

broccoli

grapes

...A Story

Write about your favourite thing to do. Draw a picture.

My Favourite Thing to Do

I like to

_____

_____

_____

_____

_____

_____

Write about a fun summer day. Draw a picture.

A Fun Summer Day
_____
_____
_____
_____
_____
_____
_____
_____
_____

...A Story

Write about a fun fall day. Draw a picture.

A Fun Fall Day

_____

_____

_____

_____

_____

_____

_____

_____

Write about a fun winter day. Draw a picture.

A Fun Winter Day

_____

_____

_____

_____

_____

_____

_____

_____

...A Story

Write about a fun spring day. Draw a picture.

A Fun Spring Day

_____

_____

_____

_____

_____

_____

_____

Solutions

Page 6

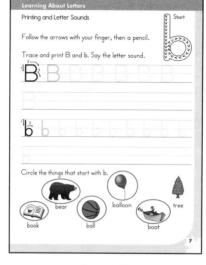

Page 7

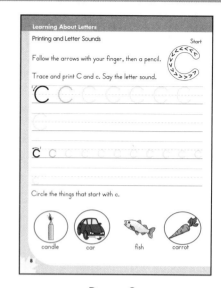

Page 8

Page 9

Page 10

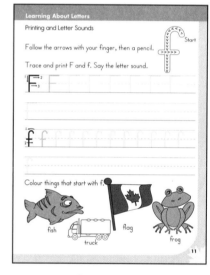

Page 11

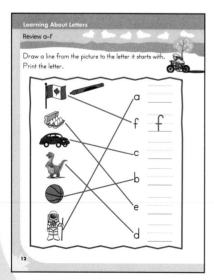

Page 12

Page 13

Page 14

Solutions

Page 15

Page 16

Page 17

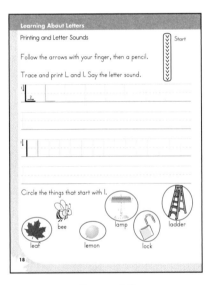

Page 18

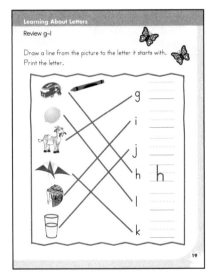

Page 19

Page 20

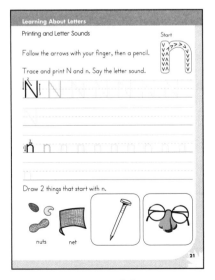

Page 21

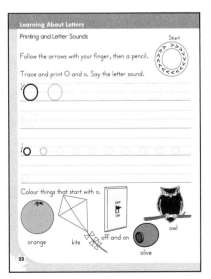

Page 22

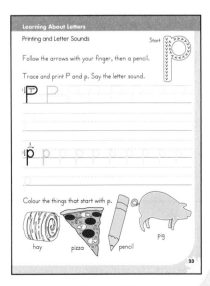

Page 23

Solutions

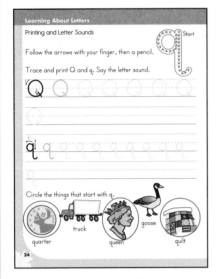

Page 24

Page 25

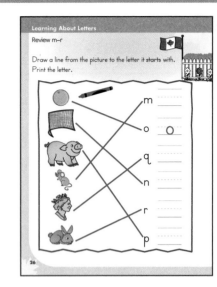

Page 26

Page 27

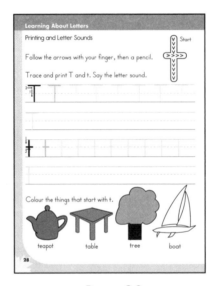

Page 28

Page 29

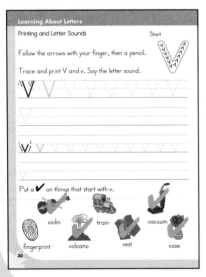

Page 30

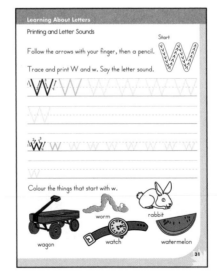

Page 31

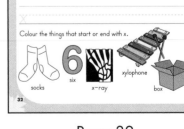

Page 32

Solutions

Page 33

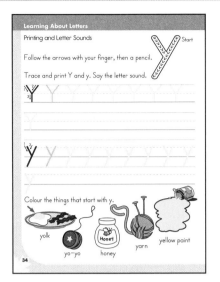

Page 34

Page 35

Page 36

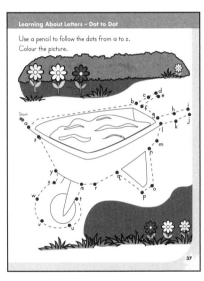

Page 37

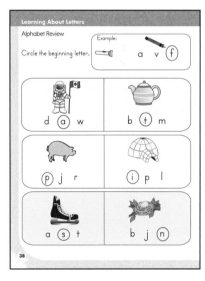

Page 38

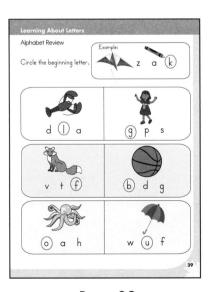

Page 39

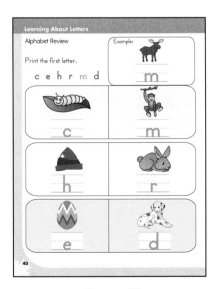

Page 40

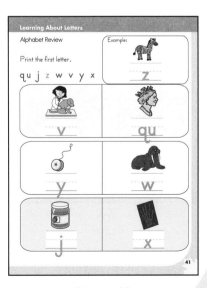

Page 41

Solutions

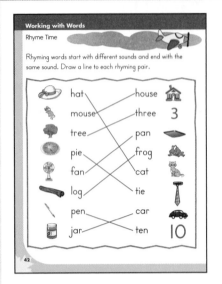

Page 42

Page 43

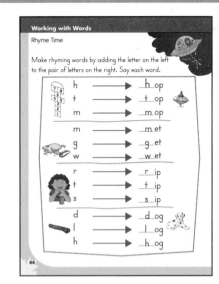

Page 44

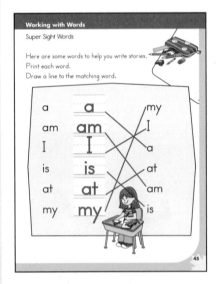

Page 45

Page 46

Page 49

Page 50

You are done!